nickelodeon

TEENAGE MUTANT NINJA TURTLES

HEAD-TO-HEAD

SCHOLASTIC

an imprint of
SCHOLASTIC
www.scholastic.com

Published by Tangerine Press, an imprint of Scholastic Inc., 557 Broadway, New York, NY 10012

Scholastic, Tangerine Press, and associated logos are trademarks and/or registered trademarks of Scholastic Inc.

Teenage Mutant Ninja Turtles Head-to-Head is produced by becker&mayer! LLC, Bellevue, WA

www.beckermayer.com

If you have questions or comments about this product, please visit www.beckermayer.com/customerservice.html and click on the Customer Service Request Form.

becker&mayer!
BOOK PRODUCERS

Written by Paul Beck
Edited by Ben Grossblatt and Nicole Burns Ascue
Designed by Rosanna Brockley
Production management by Jennifer Marx

Printed, manufactured, and assembled in New Jersey, USA

10 9 8 7 6 5 4 3 2 1

ISBN: 978-0-545-70965-1

13660

The Teenage Mutant Ninja Turtles and friends call on their martial-arts skills to fight aliens, mutants, and evil ninjas in these one-on-one fights and epic team battles. Each matchup gives a description of the opponents, along with their skills, stats, and special abilities. It's up to you to decide the winners. At the end of the book you'll find a page of experts' predictions for the matches, so you can compare your picks with theirs.

TEENAGE MUTANT NINJA TURTLES

One day in New York City, ninja master Hamato Yoshi stepped out of a pet store with four new baby turtles. A man passed him on the sidewalk. There was something strange about the man, so Yoshi followed him into an alley. There the stranger met another man, and the two exchanged a mysterious, glowing cylinder. When Yoshi surprised them in the act, they attacked him.

The ninja master fended off his attackers, but during the fight the cylinder broke and splashed Hamato Yoshi and his pet turtles with glowing green ooze. The ooze was a powerful alien mutagen. It combined Yoshi's DNA with the DNA of an alley rat, mutating him into a giant human-rodent hybrid. At the same time, the mutagen transformed the turtles with the ninja master's DNA.

Hamato Yoshi, now known as Splinter, fled into the sewers with his four young mutants. He raised the turtles as his own sons, naming them after his favorite Renaissance artists: Leonardo, Donatello, Raphael, and Michelangelo. He taught them the philosophy and martial art of ninjutsu, the way of the ninja. All the while, Master Splinter kept his sons hidden in their secret sewer lair. Only when they had the discipline to control both their minds and their bodies would he let them visit the surface.

That day finally came, and Splinter allowed the now-teenage ninjas to leave the sewers. The brothers soon found themselves in the middle of a pair of nefarious plots that still threaten their family, friends, and the very fate of the planet.

The Kraang, aliens from another dimension, are working on a plan to transform Earth into a new homeworld for themselves. The aliens are responsible for the ooze that mutated Splinter and the Turtles. Their failed mutation experiments frequently create dangerous monsters the Turtles have to stop.

And an old enemy has resurfaced after many years. The evil ninja master known as Shredder followed Hamato Yoshi, his former rival, from Japan to New York. At the head of the criminal Foot Clan, Shredder marshals his forces for an all-out attack on the Turtles and final revenge against Splinter.

Through it all, the Teenage Mutant Ninja Turtles roam the nighttime rooftops and alleys of New York, where they use their ninja skills to protect the city from criminals, aliens, and dangerous mutants.

LEONARDO VS. KARAI

Leonardo first met Karai on a New York rooftop, where she appeared out of nowhere and challenged him to a fight. She tossed blinding powder in his eyes and disappeared again. Karai is a kunoichi, or female ninja, a member of the Foot Clan, and the daughter of the Turtles' archenemy, Shredder. Leo has just a tiny bit of a crush on her.

SPECIES: Turtle-human mutant

AFFILIATION: Ninja Turtles/Splinter

HOME: Turtles' lair

MAIN WEAPONS: Katana swords

SPECIAL SKILLS: Leadership, strategy

LEONARDO

As the leader of the Turtles, Leonardo trains and studies hard in order to set an example for his brothers. He takes his leadership role seriously. He just wishes the others would do the same. Still, his brothers really do appreciate him, and his heroism has gotten them out of some tough situations.

Strength	7
Speed	8
Agility	7
Intuition	7
Chops	7
Ninjutsu mastery	7

THE SHOWDOWN

Leonardo and Karai are as evenly matched as two teenage ninjas can be. Both were raised and trained by ninjutsu masters. Both fight with katana swords. But the decisive contest here may not be between weapons, but between minds. Karai is skilled at deception, and Leo will have to hone his concentration to avoid being distracted.

SPECIES: Human
AFFILIATION: Foot Clan/Shredder
HOME: Shredder's hideout
MAIN WEAPON: Katana sword
SPECIAL SKILLS: Stealth, speed, deception

7	Strength
8	Speed
7	Agility
7	Intuition
7	Chops
7	Ninjutsu mastery

KARAI

Master Shredder raised Karai as his daughter. She's loyal to him, but she often disobeys him to carry out plans of her own. Karai's ninjutsu skills are as good as any of the Turtles'. Though she'll never admit it, deep down she feels a certain kinship with Leonardo.

Who wins? See p. 62!

RAPHAEL VS. DOGPOUND

Chris Bradford was a ninjutsu expert who ran a chain of martial-arts dojos. In secret, he was also the top henchman of the evil Shredder, master of the Foot Clan. Bradford once tried to take the Turtles down by breaking the glass cover of an alien mutagen bomb. Washed away in a river of glowing ooze, Bradford mutated into a giant dog. Now known by the mocking nickname Dogpound, he faces off against Raphael, the biggest and toughest of the Ninja Turtles.

RAPHAEL

Raphael likes a good brawl. He doesn't go for the subtle or tricky approach, preferring to charge into the middle of things with his weapons at the ready. He'll make fun of his brothers when he thinks they're being too cautious or weak, but he's the first to come to their aid when they're in trouble.

SPECIES: Turtle-human mutant
AFFILIATION: Ninja Turtles/Splinter
HOME: Turtles' lair
MAIN WEAPONS: Sai
SPECIAL SKILLS: Strength, speed

Strength	7.5
Speed	8
Agility	8.5
Intuition	7.5
Chops	5
Ninjutsu mastery	8

THE SHOWDOWN

This will be a tough battle. Not just because the opponents are expert ninjas, but also because they both fight best in close combat. Dogpound attacks with his fists, feet, and razor-sharp claws. Raphael wields a pair of sai, needle-like blades with prongs at the base. Dogpound has the advantage in size, but Raph is quicker and more agile. As long as he can keep a cool head, Raphael should be more than a match for the mutant canine.

SPECIES: Human-dog mutant
AFFILIATION: Foot Clan/Shredder
HOME: Shredder's hideout
MAIN WEAPONS: Claws, fists, feet
SPECIAL SKILLS: Ninjutsu mastery

8	Strength
7.5	Speed
7	Agility
5.5	Intuition
5	Chops
8	Ninjutsu mastery

DOGPOUND

Chris Bradford was the evil Shredder's best pupil. As master of his own dojos, Bradford recruited fighters for Shredder's army of ninjas, the Foot Clan. Now much bigger and stronger than he was as a human, Dogpound still has the master ninja skills he learned from Shredder.

Who wins? See p. 62! **11**

DONATELLO VS. BAXTER STOCKMAN

When the Turtles first met tech geek Baxter Stockman, he was trying to break into an office building while dressed in homemade, powered battle armor. Both the armor and the break-in were duds, but Stockman found the key to improving his invention: the Turtles' T-Pod music player, left behind by Mikey. A military-grade A.I. chip in the T-Pod reconfigures the battle armor into a formidable fighting machine. In this matchup, Stockman faces the Turtles' own tech wizard, Donatello.

SPECIES: Turtle-human mutant
AFFILIATION: Ninja Turtles/Splinter
HOME: Turtles' lair
MAIN WEAPON: Bo staff
SPECIAL SKILLS: Science, technology

DONATELLO

Donnie is a scientist and tech wiz. He's constantly developing new inventions for the Turtles, such as their T-Phone communicators and the Shellraiser battle vehicle. Of course he's also a highly trained ninja. His main weapon is a wooden staff called a bo. But it's no ordinary bo: a steel blade pops out of the end.

Strength	5.5
Speed	7
Agility	7.5
Intuition	7
Chops	6.5
Ninjutsu mastery	6.5

THE SHOWDOWN

Baxter Stockman is well protected inside his battle armor. The suit's powerful arms can snake out over long distances to deliver a punch or toss a Turtle across the room. The hands detach to attack on their own with claws and lasers. Donnie's best strategy will be to try to smash the T-Pod in its socket on the battle armor. Without the music player's A.I. chip, the armor will shut down. Stockman is no fighter on his own.

SPECIES: Human

AFFILIATION: Independent, sometimes forced to work for the Foot Clan

HOME: Baxter Stockman's lab

MAIN WEAPON: Robot battle armor

SPECIAL SKILLS: High tech

6.5	Strength
6	Speed
4	Agility
6.5	Intuition
1	Chops
2	Ninjutsu mastery

BAXTER STOCKMAN

Baxter Stockman is a tech geek and inventor. He started down the road to a life of crime when he got expelled from high school after burning down the gym with a real volcano at the science fair. He would be considered an evil genius if most of his plans didn't go horribly wrong.

Who wins? See p. 62!

MICHELANGELO VS. KRAATHATROGON

The Kraathatrogon are giant worms from the Kraang's home in Dimension X. The aliens brought them to Earth through their dimensional portal. The Kraathatrogon secrete mutagen through pores in their skin. The Kraang milk them like mutagen cows. Here Michelangelo faces off against a small Kraathatrogon. It's just a youngster, but it's already the size of a city bus. The truly large worms grow to 100 feet or more.

SPECIES: Turtle-human mutant
AFFILIATION: Ninja Turtles/Splinter
HOME: Turtles' lair
MAIN WEAPON: Nunchuks
SPECIAL SKILLS: Creativity, practical jokes

MICHELANGELO

Mikey is the goofiest of the four Turtle brothers. He likes jokes, tricks, and making up names for the Turtles' enemies. He's also the most creative, always coming up with new ideas. Some of his new ideas are even *good*. He's a master of the nunchuks, one of the more difficult ninja weapons.

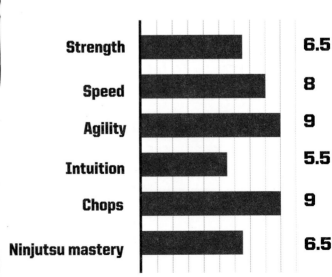

Strength	6.5
Speed	8
Agility	9
Intuition	5.5
Chops	9
Ninjutsu mastery	6.5

THE SHOWDOWN

The Kraathatrogon is big and fast. Its three jaws are lined with needle-sharp teeth. The worm will do its best to swallow Michelangelo whole. But Mikey shouldn't have much trouble dodging the charging worm. And he knows a secret: the Kraang often ride the giant worms, using their antennae as reins. If the agile and acrobatic Mikey can hop up on the Kraathatrogon's back, he just might be able to tame it and end the fight.

SPECIES: Giant worm
AFFILIATION: Kraang
HOME: Dimension X
MAIN WEAPONS: Jaws, teeth
SPECIAL SKILLS: Secretes mutagen from its skin

9	Strength
8	Speed
3	Agility
1	Intuition
4	Chops
0	Ninjutsu mastery

KRAATHATROGON

The Kraathatrogon looks like a cross between a worm and a slug. Its mouth splits into three triangular jaws with a cavernous space inside. The Kraathatrogon are the source of the mutagen that the Kraang use in their experiments. The giant worms have one weakness: they're sensitive to salt.

Who wins? See p. 62!

APRIL O'NEIL VS. FOOT CLAN NINJA

A ninja of the Foot Clan slips out of the darkness as if appearing from thin air. He fights in silence, his face invisible behind his black, bug-eyed mask. Here he faces April O'Neil. She may look like an ordinary teenager, but she has the fighting skills of a kunoichi. Even if she defeats her opponent, April will have to stay alert. Where there's one Foot, there are always others close behind.

APRIL O'NEIL

April is the teenage daughter of scientist Kirby O'Neil. She has been the Turtles' friend since the time they rescued her from a kidnapping attempt by the alien Kraang. For reasons she doesn't know, the Kraang are still after her. April studies the ways of the kunoichi, or female ninja, under Master Splinter.

SPECIES: Human
AFFILIATION: Ninja Turtles/Splinter
HOME: New York apartment
MAIN WEAPON: Metal fan known as a tessen
SPECIAL SKILLS: Agility, ability to sense things others can't

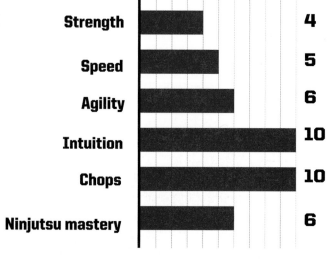

Strength	4
Speed	5
Agility	6
Intuition	10
Chops	10
Ninjutsu mastery	6

THE SHOWDOWN

With silence and speed, the Foot Clan ninja will try to take April by surprise. But April's superb senses should give her plenty of warning to meet the attack. Her ninjutsu skills make her more than a match for her opponent. The Foot's katana has a longer reach than April's tessen fan, so she'll have to block the sword and get in close to defeat him.

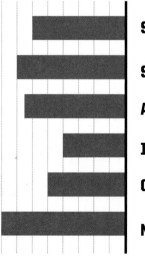

SPECIES: Human
AFFILIATION: Foot Clan/Shredder
HOME: Shredder's hideout
MAIN WEAPON: Katana sword
SPECIAL SKILLS: Stealth, speed

6	Strength
7	Speed
6.5	Agility
4	Intuition
5	Chops
8	Ninjutsu mastery

FOOT CLAN NINJA

The ninjas of the Foot Clan were originally recruited and trained in Japan by Oroku Saki, later known as Shredder. In Japan, the Foot were assassins and thieves. Now they have followed Shredder to New York, where they do their master's bidding in his battle for revenge against Splinter and the Ninja Turtles.

Who wins? See p. 62!

SPLINTER VS. SHREDDER

The rivalry between the ninja masters Splinter and Shredder goes back to their early days in Japan, when Splinter was still the human Hamato Yoshi and Shredder went by his real name, Oroku Saki. The jealous Shredder blames Splinter for stealing his one true love, Tang Shen, even though she was never really his. In Japan, Shredder's pursuit of Splinter caused the death of Tang Shen. Now he has followed Splinter to New York on a twisted quest for revenge.

SPLINTER

Splashed with mutagen ooze in a back-alley skirmish with alien Kraang robots, the human ninja master Hamato Yoshi mutated into a giant rat. He retreated into the maze of sewers and tunnels beneath New York City, along with his transformed pet turtles. Now known as Splinter, Yoshi is both father and sensei to the Teenage Mutant Ninja Turtles.

SPECIES: Human-rat mutant
AFFILIATION: Ninja Turtles
HOME: Turtles' lair
MAIN WEAPON: Staff
SPECIAL SKILLS: Ninjutsu mastery, wisdom

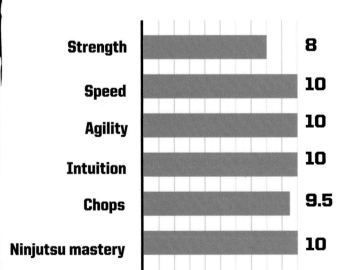

Strength	8
Speed	10
Agility	10
Intuition	10
Chops	9.5
Ninjutsu mastery	10

THE SHOWDOWN

This showdown pits Splinter's subtle, lightning-fast ninjutsu mastery against Shredder's equally skillful brute-force style. Shredder will attack like an armored freight train. That is, if freight trains brandished razor-sharp blades. But with superior speed and ratlike agility, Splinter can literally run circles around his archenemy. Shredder may be bigger and stronger, but he'll have a hard time defending himself, as the Turtles' sensei seems to attack from every direction at once.

SPECIES: Human
AFFILIATION: Foot Clan
HOME: Shredder's hideout
MAIN WEAPONS: Clawlike blades known as tekko-kagi
SPECIAL SKILLS: Immense strength, ruthlessness

8.5	Strength
9.5	Speed
9	Agility
8	Intuition
7	Chops
10	Ninjutsu mastery

SHREDDER

In Japan, Oroku Saki became the leader of the ninja Foot Clan, transforming it into a master criminal organization. His ruthless behavior earned him the name Shredder. He wears blade-encrusted samurai armor and hides his disfigured face under a masked helmet. He will stop at nothing to get revenge on his old rival, Splinter.

Who wins? See p. 62!

KIRBY BAT VS. KRAANG

When the Turtles accidentally dropped a cargo of mutagen from a Kraang stealth ship, one of the falling canisters plummeted straight toward April O'Neil and her scientist father, Kirby. The canister shattered and covered Mr. O'Neil with mutagen ooze. Surrounded by a cloud of flapping bats, Kirby mutated into a giant bat. Here he faces one of the creatures that brought the mutagen to Earth, an alien Kraang.

SPECIES: Human-bat mutant
AFFILIATION: Independent
HOME: Rooftops of New York
MAIN WEAPONS: Claws, wings, teeth
SPECIAL SKILLS: Flight

KIRBY BAT

Even as a bat, the mutant Kirby's large, domed head hints at the intelligence of the human scientist he once was. Both April and the Turtles hope his bat form is only temporary. Donatello has sworn to find a cure for the mutation. Meanwhile, Kirby flies the nighttime New York skies, waiting for his chance to reunite with his daughter.

Strength	4
Speed	5
Agility	5
Intuition	7
Chops	7
Ninjutsu mastery	0

THE SHOWDOWN

In this contest, the opponents will fight hand to hand, or, really, wing to tentacle. Kirby's flying ability and grasping feet should give him the advantage over the slithering Kraang. The bat's best strategy will be an aerial attack. For its part, the Kraang will try to wrap Kirby in its tentacles and pull him to the ground, where the alien can attack with its teeth. But Kirby can defend himself with fangs of his own.

SPECIES: Interdimensional alien
AFFILIATION: Kraang
HOME: Dimension X
MAIN WEAPONS: Tentacles, teeth
SPECIAL SKILLS: Intelligence, advanced technology

2	Strength
2	Speed
2	Agility
4	Intuition
2	Chops
0	Ninjutsu mastery

KRAANG

Pink and squishy, a Kraang looks like a cross between a naked brain and a squid, with glowing eyes and a mouthful of needle-sharp teeth. A Kraang can use its six tentacles to crawl along the ground or climb a wall, but without a vehicle or robotic body, this alien isn't much good in a fight.

Who wins? See p. 62!

THE NEWTRALIZER VS. TIGER CLAW

Returning from a trip to Japan, Master Shredder brought along a new second-in-command: Tiger Claw. The Kraang turned him into a human-tiger mutant when he was just a young boy. Now he is the most feared assassin in all of Asia. His tail is missing—that's a sensitive subject—and he has sworn revenge on the rival who cut it off. Here he faces the Newtralizer, a mutant amphibian warrior whose strength and weaponry are matched only by his hatred of the Kraang.

THE NEWTRALIZER

The Newtralizer was created from a normal newt in one of the Kraang's mutagen experiments. He was held prisoner in a Kraang research facility until he was accidentally freed by Donatello. Bristling with weapons and ready for revenge, the Newtralizer will attack anyone in his path, whether Kraang or Turtle.

SPECIES: Newt mutant

AFFILIATION: Independent

HOME: Kraang research facility

MAIN WEAPONS: Rotary machine blaster, explosive shuriken (throwing stars), tail blades

SPECIAL SKILLS: Rampant destruction

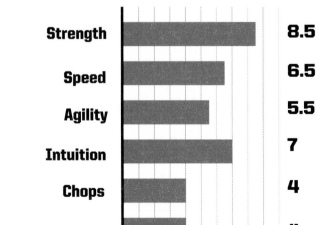

Strength	8.5
Speed	6.5
Agility	5.5
Intuition	7
Chops	4
Ninjutsu mastery	4

THE SHOWDOWN

The Newtralizer is armed to the teeth—and to the tail. Along with a huge rotary machine blaster, he carries a plasma-rope gun, explosive throwing blades, wrist lasers, and a pair of razor-sharp ax blades. Tiger Claw is a nearly even match for the mutant newt. He fights with a pair of handheld cannons. One shoots blazing bolts of energy. The other blasts rays of cold that freeze anything they touch into ice crystals.

SPECIES: Human-tiger mutant
AFFILIATION: Foot Clan/Shredder
HOME: Shredder's hideout
MAIN WEAPONS: Handheld cannons, katana sword
SPECIAL SKILLS: Flight

8	Strength
9	Speed
8.5	Agility
8	Intuition
6	Chops
8	Ninjutsu mastery

TIGER CLAW

Tiger Claw's favorite drink is skim milk. He laps it up with his tongue, but this powerful mutant is nothing like a kitten. He's an expert ninja, as deadly with a sword as he is with a blaster. He can also fly using the rocket pack he wears strapped to his back.

Who wins? See p. 62! **23**

LEATHERHEAD VS. RAHZAR

The powerful Leatherhead was created when the alien Kraang found a small alligator in the sewers. They brought the gator to their home dimension as a subject for their gruesome mutation experiments. Leatherhead eventually escaped back through the portal to Earth's own dimension, stealing the portal's power cell on the way. In this matchup the mutant alligator faces Rahzar, the twice-mutated fighter who was once the human Chris Bradford.

SPECIES: Alligator mutant
AFFILIATION: Independent
HOME: Abandoned subway platform
MAIN WEAPONS: Claws, teeth, tail
SPECIAL SKILLS: Superior strength, berserker rage

LEATHERHEAD

Leatherhead began life as a small alligator, raised as a pet by a human boy. The boy's fearful parents flushed the alligator down the toilet, and the Kraang took him from the sewer. Now the sight of a Kraangdroid—or even the mention of the name "Kraang"—sends Leatherhead into an uncontrollable rage.

Strength	9.5
Speed	8.5
Agility	5
Intuition	5
Chops	6
Ninjutsu mastery	7.5

THE SHOWDOWN

This hand-to-hand match pits Leatherhead's superior size and strength against Rahzar's agility and razor-sharp claws. The dog mutant will attack with slashing blows while trying to avoid the alligator's jaws and sweeping tail. Leatherhead's martial arts skills aren't as good, but his tough alligator hide can take a lot of punishment without serious harm. The key for Leatherhead will be to stay in the fight long enough to tire Rahzar out, then take the offensive and finish him off.

SPECIES: Human-dog double mutant
AFFILIATION: Foot Clan/Shredder
HOME: Shredder's hideout
MAIN WEAPONS: Razor claws, teeth
SPECIAL SKILLS: Superfast dog ninjutsu, ability to throw his claws

8.5	Strength
8.5	Speed
8.5	Agility
5.5	Intuition
6	Chops
9	Ninjutsu mastery

RAHZAR

As Dogpound, Chris Bradford longed for his former human body. But instead of finding a way back to his old form, he fell into a vat of mutagen and mutated even further. His new, more wolflike Rahzar body is leaner, meaner, and faster than his human body ever was.

Who wins? See p. 62!

METALHEAD VS. MOUSERS

Mobile Offensive Underground Search, Excavation, and Retrieval Sentries, or MOUSERS, are an army of podlike robot thieves unleashed on the New York underworld by techno geek Baxter Stockman. The sharp-jawed robots tunnel their way into criminals' hideouts to steal their loot. In this matchup, the MOUSERS face off against Donatello's robot ninja, Metalhead. Metalhead can't fight on his own. Donnie has to operate the robot by remote control.

SPECIES: Robot

AFFILIATION: Ninja Turtles/Splinter

HOME: Turtles' lair

MAIN WEAPONS: Laser cannon, flamethrower, detachable fists

SPECIAL SKILLS: Rocket propulsion in feet

METALHEAD

Donatello originally designed Metalhead by reverse engineering one of the Kraang robots known as Kraangdroids. Donnie operates the robot with a video-game controller. Metalhead had a few bugs at first, which let him get hijacked and used against the Turtles by the Kraang. But Donnie is constantly updating and improving his design.

Strength	7.5
Speed	7.5
Agility	7
Intuition	8
Chops	5
Ninjutsu mastery	7

THE SHOWDOWN

MOUSERS' strength is in their numbers. A single MOUSERS unit is easy to defeat, but Metalhead, with Donnie at the controls, will have his hands full when he faces a whole pack of them. The MOUSERS will mount a group attack and try to break the Turtles' robot into pieces, rendering him helpless. But Metalhead's superior weaponry, combined with Donatello's remote-control ninja skills, should be enough to balance the fight.

SPECIES: Robot

AFFILIATION: Baxter Stockman/Foot Clan/Shredder

HOME: Baxter Stockman's lab

MAIN WEAPONS: Mechanical jaws and teeth

SPECIAL SKILLS: Ability to tunnel through dirt and rock

4	Strength
5.5	Speed
6	Agility
2	Intuition
0.5	Chops
0	Ninjutsu mastery

MOUSERS

Baxter Stockman created his horde of two-legged mechanical minions to steal loot and make him rich. As a bonus, the robots will pursue and attack anyone who has been tagged with a special MOUSERS-attracting radioisotope spray. The spray won't wash off, and the little robots will never give up the chase.

Who wins? See p. 62!

CASEY JONES VS. KRAANGDROIDS

When you're trying to take over the Earth, it's hard to get much done if you're as weak and squishy as the Kraang. So for fighting, working, and just plain getting around, these aliens ride in the abdomens of humanoid robots called Kraangdroids. They're just the kind of evildoers Casey Jones has sworn to clear off the New York streets. With hockey-stick weapons and goalie pads for armor, he'll bring his homegrown fighting skills to the battle.

CASEY JONES

Casey is a student at April O'Neil's high school. He first entered the Turtles' world when April began tutoring him in math after school. Casey has no formal ninja training. His fighting skills are all self-taught, but he practices diligently. Raphael tells him that as a fighter Casey is "raw, unfocused, dangerous, crazy, but not bad."

SPECIES: Human
AFFILIATION: Independent
HOME: New York apartment above a barbershop
MAIN WEAPONS: Hockey sticks, pucks, homemade high-voltage zapper
SPECIAL SKILLS: Skating

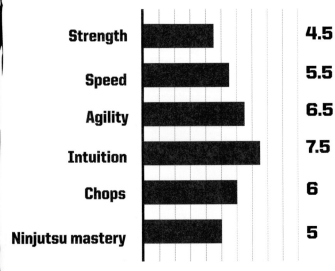

Strength	4.5
Speed	5.5
Agility	6.5
Intuition	7.5
Chops	6
Ninjutsu mastery	5

THE SHOWDOWN

In their usual way, the Kraangdroids will charge together with blasters blazing. Casey will have to rely on his skating speed to dodge the laser bolts. A well-placed hockey puck can take an android down from a distance, but if he can get in close enough, he'll be able to use his high-voltage zapper to short out the robots' electrical systems. For their part, the Kraangdroids will try to overwhelm Casey with sheer numbers.

SPECIES: Robot
AFFILIATION: Kraang
HOME: The TCRI building
MAIN WEAPONS: Blasters
SPECIAL SKILLS: Robotic strength, speed

4.5	Strength
3.5	Speed
3	Agility
3	Intuition
1	Chops
0	Ninjutsu mastery

KRAANGDROIDS

Each Kraangdroid serves as a mechanical body for a brainlike Kraang. The Kraang pilots the robot from a cockpit in the Kraangdroid's abdomen. They can fire blasters, but they're not much good in a hand-to-hand fight. If the robot is disabled, the Kraang will try to get away from the action on its tentacles.

Who wins? See p. 62!

APRIL AND DONATELLO VS. FISHFACE

Master Shredder's mutant minion Fishface is a fish out of water, but that doesn't get in his way. He stalks the streets on a pair of robotic legs, stronger and faster than the natural ones he had as a human. A pair of tanks keeps his gills supplied with water, and he has a venomous bite. Here the fish faces off against the double team of April O'Neil and Donatello.

APRIL AND DONATELLO

Master Splinter's two smartest pupils team up for a formidable combination of brains and ninjutsu skills. Donnie has more training, but April has learned her fighting skills from the same sensei. April's intuition and ability to read her opponents, along with her kunoichi mastery of deception, make this a well-rounded team for any fight.

SPECIES: Human and Turtle-human mutant
AFFILIATION: Ninja Turtles/Splinter
HOME: Turtles' lair
MAIN WEAPONS: Tessen fan, bo staff
TEAM STRENGTHS: Intelligence, intuition

Strength	6
Speed	6
Agility	7
Intuition	8.5
Chops	8.5
Ninjutsu mastery	6

THE SHOWDOWN

Fishface is a tough and nasty customer. His web-fingered fists and robotic legs are more than a match for April's tessen and Donatello's bo. The teenagers will do best if they split up and come at the mutant fish from two different directions. Donnie will have to be careful not to let his well-known crush on April make him overprotective, distracting him from the battle. April can hold her own in this fight.

SPECIES: Human-fish mutant
AFFILIATION: Foot Clan/Shredder
HOME: Shredder's hideout
MAIN WEAPONS: Fish fists, robotic ninja legs
SPECIAL SKILLS: Venomous bite

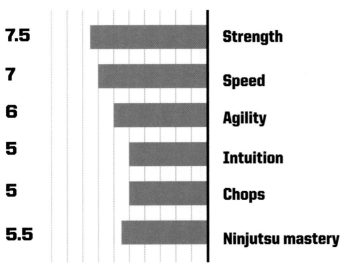

7.5	Strength
7	Speed
6	Agility
5	Intuition
5	Chops
5.5	Ninjutsu mastery

FISHFACE

When he got caught in the same torrent of ooze that turned Chris Bradford into a dog, Shredder's Brazilian henchman Xever mutated into a giant fish. Using Kraang technology, tech wiz Baxter Stockman fitted Fishface with a pair of robotic legs and gill tanks, so the mutant fish can travel and fight on land.

Who wins? See p. 62! **31**

LEONARDO AND DONATELLO VS. RAPHAEL AND MICHELANGELO

As part of their training, the Teenage Mutant Ninja Turtles spend many hours sparring each other in Master Splinter's dojo. For this matchup, Leo and Donnie team up against Raph and Mikey. Master Splinter will give the signal for the fight to begin: "Hajime!"

SPECIES: Turtle-human mutants
AFFILIATION: Ninja Turtles/Splinter
HOME: Turtles' lair
MAIN WEAPONS: Katana swords, bo staff
SPECIAL SKILLS: Planning, strategy

LEONARDO AND DONATELLO

Leo and Donnie are the thinkers of the group. This team has a brainy fighting style, with Donnie analyzing all the possible moves in the match and Leo planning the attack. Surprises may trip this team up, but planning and strategy could win the match.

Strength	7
Speed	7.5
Agility	8.5
Intuition	7
Chops	8
Ninjutsu mastery	7.5

THE SHOWDOWN

This matchup splits up the two best fighters, Leo and Raph, so neither team has an unfair advantage. The brothers all know one another's fighting styles. Each team is good at predicting what their opponents will do, so the match will come down to a contest of pure ninjutsu skill.

SPECIES: Turtle-human mutants
AFFILIATION: Ninja Turtles/Splinter
HOME: Turtles' lair
MAIN WEAPONS: Sai, nunchuks
SPECIAL SKILLS: Strength, creativity

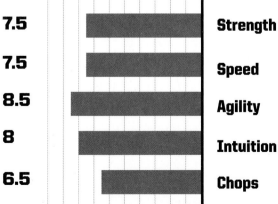

7.5	Strength
7.5	Speed
8.5	Agility
8	Intuition
6.5	Chops
7.5	Ninjutsu mastery

RAPHAEL AND MICHELANGELO

In a fight, Raph tends to charge in without thinking. Usually his strength and speed make up for any lack of strategy, but his opponents may be able to take advantage of his emotional fighting style. Mikey isn't as strong a fighter, but he often comes up with unusual or unexpected moves.

Who wins? See p. 62! **33**

APRIL AND CASEY JONES VS. MUTAGEN MAN

Ninja wannabe Timothy, better known as the Pulverizer, was a fumble-footed doofus. He doused himself with mutagen in the hope of gaining superhero powers. Instead he mutated into a giant blob confined to a glass tank in the Turtles' lair. Later, powered by more mutagen, Timothy grew gelatinous arms and legs and went on the rampage. In this matchup, high-school classmates April O'Neil and Casey Jones team up to battle Timothy, otherwise known as Mutagen Man.

APRIL AND CASEY JONES

In this team April is the one with formal kunoichi training, learned from her sensei, Master Splinter. She's also the brains of the team. Casey is self-taught, a ferocious fighter but undisciplined. His hockey puck slap shots should keep Timothy busy while April devises a way to bring Mutagen Man under control.

SPECIES: Human
AFFILIATION: Ninja Turtles/Independent
HOME: Roosevelt High School
MAIN WEAPONS: Tessen fan, hockey sticks, pucks
TEAM STRENGTHS: Intelligence, intuition, speed

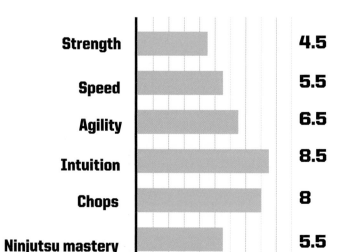

Strength	4.5
Speed	5.5
Agility	6.5
Intuition	8.5
Chops	8
Ninjutsu mastery	5.5

THE SHOWDOWN

Mutagen Man isn't evil. He wants to be April's friend, but he's very, very jealous. Deranged by the effects of mutagen, he strikes out at everyone around him. Weapons have little effect. He just grabs them in his huge hands and dissolves them with acid. He's much stronger than April and Casey, but he needs a constant supply of mutagen for energy. The teenagers' best strategy will be to keep him distracted until he runs out of mutagen and loses energy.

SPECIES: Human mutant
AFFILIATION: Independent
HOME: Turtles' lair
MAIN WEAPONS: Hands, feet, acid
SPECIAL SKILLS: Can dissolve weapons

9	Strength
6	Speed
4	Agility
2.5	Intuition
3	Chops
0	Ninjutsu mastery

MUTAGEN MAN

Timothy, the former Pulverizer, is now a tankful of gelatinous green goo. His eyes, mouth, brain, and other organs can be seen floating around inside. His powerful, gooey arms and legs protrude from valves on the outside of the tank. His only other weapon is the acid inside his body.

Who wins? See p. 62!

LEONARDO AND RAPHAEL VS. APRIL DERP

Deep inside their lab in the TCRI Building, the Kraang have been trying to clone April O'Neil. But one of their experiments went horribly wrong. The result is a giant, mutated version of April. This towering mutant is extra strong but also extra stupid. The most intelligent thing it can say is "Derp." In this matchup, the mutant April Derp goes up against the Turtle team of Leonardo and Raphael.

LEONARDO AND RAPHAEL

This double team puts together the Turtles' two most highly skilled fighters. Their styles are different: Leo tends to weigh his options in a fight, while Raph charges first and does his thinking later. Their different approaches sometimes clash, but they usually fit together, making these two a seamless fighting unit.

SPECIES: Turtle-human mutants
AFFILIATION: Ninja Turtles/Splinter
HOME: Turtles' lair
MAIN WEAPONS: Katana swords, sai
SPECIAL SKILLS: A balance of careful planning and wild impulse

Strength	8
Speed	8
Agility	8.5
Intuition	7.5
Chops	6
Ninjutsu mastery	8

THE SHOWDOWN

April Derp will come out swinging. And grabbing. And hugging. Leo and Raph will have to stay out of her reach to avoid being squashed. The mutant April's left hand and right foot are extra large and blobby, with heavy crushing power. She also has a prehensile tongue that can grab her opponents and reel them in to be squeezed. The Turtles' best strategy will be to separate, so that one of them can attack while April Derp goes after the other.

SPECIES: Human mutant

AFFILIATION: Kraang

HOME: Reject bin at the TCRI lab

MAIN WEAPONS: Hands, feet, prehensile tongue

SPECIAL SKILLS: Deadly hug

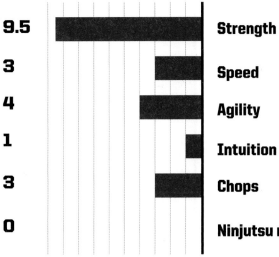

9.5	Strength
3	Speed
4	Agility
1	Intuition
3	Chops
0	Ninjutsu mastery

APRIL DERP

This misshapen mutant is three times the size of the real April. She has an extra head, mismatched arms and legs, and a spare mouth in the middle of her back. With a cry of "April hug!" April Derp tries to grab her enemies in a bone-crushing embrace.

Who wins? See p. 62!

LEONARDO AND DONATELLO VS. RAT KING

Blinded in a horrible explosion while experimenting with mutagen, evil scientist Victor Falco sent out a psychic call for help. He was rescued by rats and became the Rat King, connected by a psychic link to every sewer rat in New York. This matchup pits the mutant Rat King against the mutant turtles Leonardo and Donatello.

SPECIES: Turtle-human mutants
AFFILIATION: Ninja Turtles/Splinter
HOME: Turtles' lair
MAIN WEAPONS: Katana swords, bo staff
SPECIAL SKILLS: Quick planning, scientific analysis

LEONARDO AND DONATELLO

These two are brainy fighters. Leonardo can quickly analyze the fight and come up with a strategy for beating their opponent. Donatello's knowledge of science and scientific methods may help him get inside the mind of the scientist Falco. Of course, they're both also top-notch ninja fighters.

Strength	7
Speed	7.5
Agility	7.5
Intuition	7
Chops	7
Ninjutsu mastery	7

THE SHOWDOWN

The Rat King won't fight the Turtles himself. Instead, he'll use the eyes, bodies, and teeth of the horde of rats under his psychic control. Leo and Donnie will have to battle their way through a wave of rats to get to their opponent. If they succeed, they'll have little trouble finishing off the Rat King himself. On his own, without his rat minions to help, the blind Victor Falco is no match for a pair of trained ninjas.

SPECIES: Human mutant

AFFILIATION: Independent

HOME: The sewer

MAIN WEAPONS: Rats

SPECIAL SKILLS: Psychic connection to all the sewer rats in New York

3	Strength
2	Speed
1	Agility
7	Intuition
8	Chops
0	Ninjutsu mastery

THE RAT KING

The mutagen explosion transformed Victor Falco into a living skeleton. Though blind, Falco has millions of eyes all over New York: the eyes of the city's sewer rats. No fighter himself, the Rat King attacks through his pack of scrabbling rat minions.

Who wins? See p. 62!

LEONARDO AND MICHELANGELO VS. FOOTBOTS

In his quest for more powerful ninja warriors, Master Shredder allied himself with the alien Kraang. The Kraang gave him FootBots, robot ninjas with lightning-fast fighting skills and a built-in arsenal of deadly weapons. But the FootBots' most dangerous skill is their ability to learn in mere seconds the fighting styles that even the best ninja must study for years. Leo and Mikey have a big challenge ahead when they face this team of robot fighters.

LEONARDO AND MICHELANGELO

As a team, Leonardo and Michelangelo have an even balance of strategic planning and just going with the flow. Leo has better ninjutsu skills, but Mikey's natural style of fighting without thinking is perfect for outwitting the FootBots' artificial intelligence.

SPECIES: Turtle-human mutants
AFFILIATION: Ninja Turtles/Splinter
HOME: Turtles' lair
MAIN WEAPONS: Katana swords, nunchuks
SPECIAL SKILLS: Planning, creativity

Skill	Rating
Strength	7
Speed	7.5
Agility	8.5
Intuition	7.5
Chops	8
Ninjutsu mastery	8

THE SHOWDOWN

The FootBots were trained in ninjutsu by Shredder's daughter, Karai. With their skills and the ability to adapt to any fighting style, the robots seem invincible. The key to beating the FootBots is to be unpredictable. Leonardo, always planning and calculating, may have a difficult time with that.

SPECIES: Robot
AFFILIATION: Foot Clan/Shredder
HOME: Shredder's hideout
MAIN WEAPONS: Blades, circular saw, drill, spiked mace
SPECIAL SKILLS: Instantly learn their opponents' fighting moves

6.5	Strength
9	Speed
9.5	Agility
8.5	Intuition
7.5	Chops
8	Ninjutsu mastery

FOOTBOTS

On the outside, FootBots look like regular Foot Clan ninjas. But under their masks and clothes, they're sophisticated Kraang robots. Each FootBot has an extra, hidden pair of arms. The robots bristle with more built-in blades and tools than a Swiss army knife. They can learn their enemies' fighting styles in a matter of seconds.

Who wins? See p. 62! **41**

RAPHAEL AND DONATELLO VS.
FOOT CLAN AND KRAANGDROIDS

From time to time, the Kraang team up with Master Shredder and his minions. Shredder gets high-tech weapons in his quest for revenge against Master Splinter, and the Kraang get help in keeping the meddling Turtles out of their plans to mutate the Earth. In this matchup, the foot soldiers of both evil allies join forces to face a double Turtle team. It's Foot Clan weapons and Kraangdroid blasters against the ninjutsu skills of Raphael and Donatello.

SPECIES: Turtle-human mutants
AFFILIATION: Ninja Turtles/Splinter
HOME: Turtles' lair
MAIN WEAPONS: Sai, bo staff
SPECIAL SKILLS: Strength, speed, scientific knowledge

RAPHAEL AND DONATELLO

Raph's and Donnie's different fighting styles complement each other making this a formidable duo. Raphael tends to charge in first and think later. His superior speed and strength will be more than a match for the Foot Clan. Donatello's logical thinking and high-tech knowledge will help him against the robotic Kraangdroids.

Skill	Rating
Strength	7.5
Speed	8
Agility	8.5
Intuition	7.5
Chops	6
Ninjutsu mastery	7.5

THE SHOWDOWN

The Foot Clan will drop in seemingly out of nowhere for hand-to-hand combat. Meanwhile, the Kraangdroids will try to surround the Turtles and then fire away with their blasters. Raph and Donnie will do best if they can fend off the Foot Clan long enough to take out the robots. Without their android bodies, the Kraang are no threat in the fight. Then the Turtles can turn their attention to mopping up the Foot Clan.

SPECIES: Human, robot
AFFILIATION: Foot Clan/Shredder, Kraang
HOME: Shredder's lair, Kraang headquarters
MAIN WEAPONS: Katana swords, blasters
SPECIAL SKILLS: Stealth, speed, alien technology

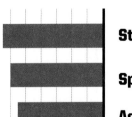

6.5	Strength
6	Speed
5.5	Agility
5	Intuition
4	Chops
6	Ninjutsu mastery

FOOT CLAN AND KRAANGDROIDS

The human Foot Clan and the robotic Kraangdroids have two different ways of fighting. In the confusing, hand-to-hand melee, the Krangdroids will have to take care not to hit their own allies with their blasters. For their part, the Foot Clan ninjas will need to leave an open line of fire for the robots.

Who wins? See p. 62! **43**

RAPHAEL AND MICHELANGELO VS. SQUIRRELANOIDS

When a squirrel gets into a puddle of mutagen ooze, the rodent seems unaffected. But things get weird when the squirrel turns into two, and they start to glow. And then things *really* heat up when the squirrels transform into powerful, vicious Squirrelanoids. This time it's up to Raphael and Michelangelo to face the menacing rodent mutants.

SPECIES: Turtle-human mutants

AFFILIATION: Ninja Turtles/Splinter

HOME: Turtles' lair

MAIN WEAPONS: Sai, nunchuks

SPECIAL SKILLS: Strength, creativity, knowledge of comic books

RAPHAEL AND MICHELANGELO

Raphael has an unpleasant history with Squirrelanoids. He was an unwilling host whose stomach served as a squirrel incubator. Michelangelo has inside knowledge of a different kind. One of his comic books describes aliens that are eerily similar to the Squirrelanoids. Clues from the comic may help the Turtles predict these mutants' behavior.

Skill	Rating
Strength	7
Speed	8
Agility	9
Intuition	6.5
Chops	7.5
Ninjutsu mastery	7.5

THE SHOWDOWN

The Squirrelanoids attack with claws, teeth, and prehensile tongues. Their tongues can shoot far out of their mouths, and at the tip there's a second squirrel head with snapping teeth. Squirrelanoids are equally at home on two or four legs. If Raph and Mikey want to stay on top of this fight, they'll have to keep alert. With giant tails for balance, the Squirrelanoids have squirrel-like climbing and jumping abilities. They can ambush their foes at any time, seemingly out of nowhere.

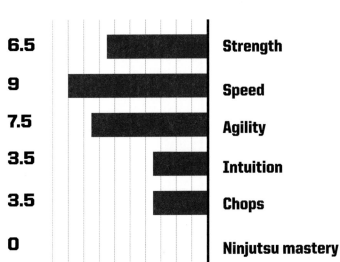

SPECIES: Squirrel mutants
AFFILIATION: Independent
HOME: The sewers
MAIN WEAPONS: Claws, teeth, prehensile tongues
SPECIAL SKILLS: Squirrel-like agility and climbing skills

6.5	Strength
9	Speed
7.5	Agility
3.5	Intuition
3.5	Chops
0	Ninjutsu mastery

SQUIRRELANOIDS

These mutants look like giant, skeletal squirrels with extra-long heads. The skulls are transparent, with the brains visible inside, floating in glowing green fluid. The glow shines out from the Squirrelanoids' mouths and eyes. Sharp teeth line the mutants' mouths, with a pair of extra-large squirrel fangs at the tip of the upper jaw.

Who wins? See p. 62! **45**

DONATELLO AND MICHELANGELO VS. SNAKEWEED

Snake was a petty thug who worked for the Kraang. When a broken mutagen canister splashed him with ooze, the Kraang henchman mutated into a giant human-plant hybrid. Now Snakeweed stalks the New York streets. The Turtles have stopped him twice, and now Donatello and Michelangelo are going to try to finish him for good.

DONATELLO AND MICHELANGELO

Among the Turtles, Donnie and Mikey sometimes feel as if they're treated like the B-team. Leonardo and Raphael do have more advanced fighting skills, but they can't match Donatello's tech and science skills or Michelangelo's intuition and creativity. And Donnie and Mikey do have mad ninjutsu skills of their own.

SPECIES: Turtle-human mutants
AFFILIATION: Ninja Turtles/Splinter
HOME: Turtles' lair
MAIN WEAPONS: Bo staff, nunchuks
SPECIAL SKILLS: Science and tech knowledge, creative thinking

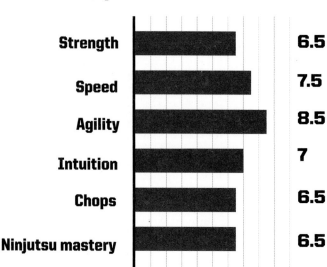

Strength	6.5
Speed	7.5
Agility	8.5
Intuition	7
Chops	6.5
Ninjutsu mastery	6.5

THE SHOWDOWN

Snakeweed's whip-like vines can thrash out over long distances to wrap around his opponents. He'll try to squeeze the Turtles in these tendrils or crush them in his claws. The way to handle a weed is to cut it down, so the Turtles will have to attack with Mikey's nunchuks and the pop-out blades in Donnie's bo staff. It will take a lot of chopping. Snakeweed's limbs grow back with weed-like speed.

SPECIES: Human-plant mutant

AFFILIATION: Independent, formerly with the Kraang

HOME: Snakeweed's lair

MAIN WEAPONS: Vine-like tentacles, claws, thorns

SPECIAL SKILLS: Can regrow severed limbs and other body parts

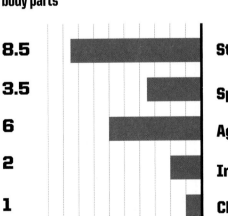

8.5	Strength
3.5	Speed
6	Agility
2	Intuition
1	Chops
0	Ninjutsu mastery

SNAKEWEED

Snakeweed looks like a cross between a praying mantis and an artichoke, with a bit of Venus flytrap thrown in. He wraps his enemies in vine-like tentacles, two of them tipped with snapping claws. In his stalk, the heart of the man he once was can still be seen, beating.

Who wins? See p. 62!

RAPHAEL, DONATELLO, AND MICHELANGELO VS. SPIDER BYTEZ AND SPY ROACH

When an obnoxious man named Vic got soaked with mutagen, he transformed into the irritating mutant known as Spider Bytez. The Spy Roach was a cockroach with spy armor, transformed by mutagen into a seamless combination of giant insect and machine. Here the arthropod mutants team up against Raph, Donnie, and Mikey.

SPECIES: Turtle-human mutants
AFFILIATION: Ninja Turtles/Splinter
HOME: Turtles' lair
MAIN WEAPONS: Sai, bo staff, nunchuks
SPECIAL SKILLS: Strength, intelligence, creativity

RAPHAEL. DONATELLO. AND MICHELANGELO

Although Raphael is the strongest fighter on this three-Turtle team, he's also the one with the biggest challenges in this matchup. Raph gets angry and loses concentration easily, so he'll have to ignore Spider Bytez's insults. And he's got a phobia about cockroaches, so he'll have to conquer his own fear as well as Spy Roach.

Strength		7
Speed		7.5
Agility		8.5
Intuition		8
Chops		7
Ninjutsu mastery		8

THE SHOWDOWN

In this fight, Spider Bytez will hang back and spit acid blobs while the nearly indestructible Spy Roach pursues the Turtles for close-in fighting. To beat the bugs, the Turtles will have to concentrate on Spy Roach first. If they don't defeat it quickly enough, it will molt, shedding its skin and transforming into its larger, flying form.

SPECIES: Human-spider and cockroach-machine mutants

AFFILIATION: Independent

HOME: Kraang research facility

MAIN WEAPONS: Fangs, claws, blaster, saw

SPECIAL SKILLS: Insults, acid-spitting, infrared vision

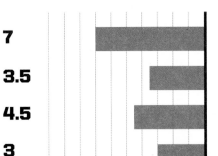

7	Strength
3.5	Speed
4.5	Agility
3	Intuition
2	Chops
0	Ninjutsu mastery

SPIDER BYTEZ AND SPY ROACH

Spider Bytez has a tarantula-like body with six eyes, fangs, and four extra spider legs growing from the top of his head. He's a champion with insults. He also spits blobs of acid goo. Spy Roach has everything you'd expect in a giant cyborg insect, including infrared camera vision, a laser blaster, and a built-in circular saw.

Who wins? See p. 62!

LEONARDO, DONATELLO, AND MICHELANGELO VS. RAHZAR AND FISHFACE

Rahzar is a double mutant. While pursuing Michelangelo in Baxter Stockman's lab, the human-dog mutant Dogpound fell into Stockman's vat of Kraang mutagen. The former Chris Bradford emerged from his second mutagen bath as a terrifying, razor-faced skeleton. Mikey named him Rahzar. In this team matchup, he fights alongside his Foot Clan comrade, Fishface. Leo, Donnie, and Mikey battle against them as a triple Turtle team.

SPECIES: Turtle-human mutants
AFFILIATION: Ninja Turtles/Splinter
HOME: Turtles' lair
MAIN WEAPONS: Katana swords, bo staff, nunchuks
SPECIAL SKILLS: Planning, intelligence, creativity

LEONARDO, DONATELLO, AND MICHELANGELO

This Turtle team is strong on brains and creativity. They'll need those if they're going to defeat Rahzar and Fishface without Raphael's brawling strength. Rahzar has all of Chris Bradford's ninjutsu mastery, but in a new, more powerful body. It's next to impossible to overpower him, so the Turtles will have to outwit him.

Skill	Rating
Strength	7
Speed	7.5
Agility	8.5
Intuition	7.5
Chops	8
Ninjutsu mastery	7.5

THE SHOWDOWN

The Turtles face familiar opponents in this matchup. But this isn't the old Dogpound that they're used to fighting. Wickedly fast and powerful, Rahzar is the stronger member of this Foot Clan duo. He'll lead the attack, while Fishface will likely hang back to harass the Turtles from the rear. The Turtles' best strategy will be for Leo and Mikey to double-team Rahzar, while Donnie takes care of Fishface.

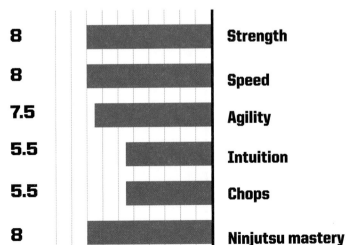

SPECIES: Human-dog double mutant and human-fish mutant
AFFILIATION: Foot Clan/Shredder
HOME: Shredder's hideout
MAIN WEAPONS: Claws, teeth, fish fists, robotic legs
SPECIAL SKILLS: Super-fast dog ninjutsu, venomous fish bite

8	Strength
8	Speed
7.5	Agility
5.5	Intuition
5.5	Chops
8	Ninjutsu mastery

RAHZAR AND FISHFACE

The doubly-mutated Chris Bradford is now nothing but bones, teeth, razor-sharp claws, and glowing yellow eyes. He's lighter, faster, and stronger than he was as a human or in his old, fleshed-out dog form. Fishface fights alongside the more powerful Rahzar, but the mutant man-fish still longs for his old human body.

Who wins? See p. 62! **51**

LEONARDO, RAPHAEL, AND MICHELANGELO VS. KRAANG BIOTROID

Aboard the Kraang's stealth ship, the Turtles discovered the Biotroid, an immense robot combining animal and machine parts. Like other Kraang robots, the Biotroid functions as a mechanical body for a brain-like Kraang. This time the Biotroid will square off against the Turtle team of Leo, Raph, and Mikey.

SPECIES: Turtle-human mutants
AFFILIATION: Ninja Turtles/Splinter
HOME: Turtles' lair
MAIN WEAPONS: Katana swords, sai, nunchuks
SPECIAL SKILLS: Speed, strength, intuition

LEONARDO, RAPHAEL, AND MICHELANGELO

This triple-Turtle combination faces a big challenge in this matchup. Without Donnie's high-tech skills and tools to use against the Biotroid, the team must rely on its well-practiced ninja fighting tactics to win. After all, an enemy is an enemy, whether human, mutant, or machine.

Skill	Rating
Strength	7
Speed	8
Agility	8.5
Intuition	7.5
Chops	7
Ninjutsu mastery	8

THE SHOWDOWN

The Biotroid will try to clobber the Turtles with its massive fists. It will slice at them with electric saws. And it will turn its back to blast away with its rear-mounted butt cannons. The Turtle trio's best strategy will be to try to get in close enough to pry the Kraang pilot out of his cockpit, which should make the Biotroid easy to bring down.

SPECIES: Robot
AFFILIATION: Kraang
HOME: Kraang stealth ship
MAIN WEAPONS: Fists, saw tentacles, butt cannons
SPECIAL SKILLS: Robot gorilla strength

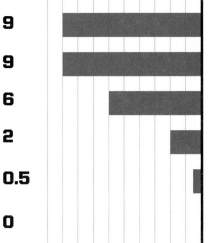

9	Strength
9	Speed
6	Agility
2	Intuition
0.5	Chops
0	Ninjutsu mastery

KRAANG BIOTROID

The Biotroid looks like a blue gorilla with a Kraang controller riding in the cockpit at the top. Its long arms pack a powerful punch. Saw-tipped steel cables spring out of its chest. And at the back, a cover on the Biotroid's rump comes off to reveal a pair of high-powered cannons.

Who wins? See p. 62!

LEONARDO, RAPHAEL, AND DONATELLO VS. SLASH

When Raph's pet turtle, Spike, came in contact with a puddle of spilled mutagen ooze, he mutated into a giant armored turtle calling himself Slash. He soon started on his plan: getting rid of Raph's three brothers, permanently. In this matchup, Slash fights Leonardo, Raphael, and Donatello.

LEONARDO, RAPHAEL, AND DONATELLO

For this match, Raph teams up with two of his brothers to battle his former pet. It takes three regular Ninja Turtles to match Slash's immense size and strength. Their skill and speed should balance out Slash's brute force and power.

SPECIES: Turtle-human mutants
AFFILIATION: Ninja Turtles/Splinter
HOME: Turtles' lair
MAIN WEAPONS: Katana swords, sai, bo staff
SPECIAL SKILLS: Speed, finely honed ninjutsu training

Strength	7
Speed	8
Agility	8.5
Intuition	7.5
Chops	7.5
Ninjutsu mastery	7.5

THE SHOWDOWN

When he was Raph's pet turtle, Slash had the chance to watch the ninja brothers train for many hours. He knows all their moves, strengths, and weaknesses. Against any one of them alone, Slash would be the hands-down winner. But now he faces three Turtles at once. Teamwork will be the key for the brothers to handle their bigger, stronger opponent.

SPECIES: Turtle mutant
AFFILIATION: Independent
HOME: Turtles' lair
MAIN WEAPONS: Spiked mace, brass knuckles
SPECIAL SKILLS: Immense strength

9	Strength
6	Speed
5	Agility
4	Intuition
4	Chops
7	Ninjutsu mastery

SLASH

The massive Slash towers over the other Turtles. His body bulges with the muscles of a wrestler. Dinosaur-like spikes cover his extra-thick armored shell. He likes his weapons prickly too, swinging a heavy mace with a wicked spiked head. His mouth has the serrated jaws of a snapping turtle.

Who wins? See p. 62!

LEONARDO, RAPHAEL, DONATELLO, AND MICHELANGELO VS. SPLINTER

All four Teenage Mutant Ninja Turtles try to best their sensei in this randori match. *Randori* is a type of ninjutsu practice, where one ninja defends himself against many attackers. Here Master Splinter faces off against the brothers to test their skills and teamwork. Four against one might not seem fair, but don't worry: even with his masterly skill and self-control, Splinter won't hurt his pupils. Not permanently, anyway.

SPECIES: Turtle-human mutants
AFFILIATION: Ninja Turtles/Splinter
HOME: Turtles' lair
MAIN WEAPONS: Katana swords, sai, bo staff, nunchuks
SPECIAL SKILLS: Four-Turtle ninjutsu

LEONARDO, RAPHAEL, DONATELLO, AND MICHELANGELO

This matchup combines all the strengths and skills of the four ninja brothers into one tough Turtle team. With Leo coordinating the battle, the Turtles' individual ninjutsu styles should work together like the gears of a well-oiled fighting machine.

Strength	7
Speed	8
Agility	8.5
Intuition	8
Chops	7
Ninjutsu mastery	8

THE SHOWDOWN

Most encounters between the brothers and their master end with the Turtles flying through the air and smashing into walls. With his rat-sharp senses and lightning speed, Master Splinter seems to anticipate where the Turtles will be almost before they know it themselves. If the brothers want the fight to last more than a few seconds, they'll have to plan carefully and coordinate their attack. Only with teamwork will the four stand a chance against the one.

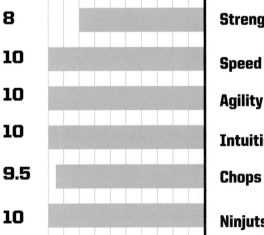

SPECIES: Human-rat mutant
AFFILIATION: Ninja Turtles
HOME: Turtles' lair
MAIN WEAPON: Staff
SPECIAL SKILLS: Ninjutsu mastery, wisdom

8	Strength
10	Speed
10	Agility
10	Intuition
9.5	Chops
10	Ninjutsu mastery

SPLINTER

Master Splinter taught the Turtles everything they know, but he hasn't taught them everything *he* knows. And because he has trained the four brothers all their lives, he knows all their strengths and weaknesses. His speed, strength, and skills are more than a match for anything his pupils can throw at him.

Who wins? See p. 62!

LEONARDO, RAPHAEL, DONATELLO, MICHELANGELO, AND APRIL VS. CHROME DOME

When Master Shredder joined forces with the Kraang, the aliens agreed to build him a powerful robot fighter. The result was the giant ninja-bot Chrome Dome. Shredder wants to use the robot to eliminate Splinter and the Turtles. But the Kraang included a few safeguards in Chrome Dome's programming, just in case Shredder's plans differ from their own. Here the android faces off against April and all four Turtles.

LEONARDO, RAPHAEL, DONATELLO, MICHELANGELO, AND APRIL

In this matchup, all of Master Splinter's pupils join together in one team. Although April can hold her own in the fight, the Turtles will be making sure she doesn't run into trouble. The robot's main objective will be to kidnap April.

SPECIES: Turtle-human mutants and human
AFFILIATION: Ninja Turtles/Splinter
HOME: Turtles' lair
MAIN WEAPONS: Katana swords, sai, bo staff, nunchuks, tessen fan
SPECIAL SKILLS: Speed, strength, creativity, intuition

Strength	6.5
Speed	7.5
Agility	8
Intuition	8.5
Chops	8
Ninjutsu mastery	7.5

THE SHOWDOWN

The Turtles and April have a hidden advantage in this fight. Chrome Dome belongs to Shredder, but the robot's Kraang designers included a secret software override that prevents Chrome Dome from harming April. Of course, that's because the Kraang want to kidnap her for a mysterious purpose of their own. April should be safe in the battle, but the team will have to make sure Chrome Dome doesn't try to grab her and escape.

SPECIES: Robot

AFFILIATION: Foot Clan/Shredder

HOME: Shredder's hideout

MAIN WEAPONS: Plasma whip, plasma sword, eye lasers

SPECIAL SKILLS: Foot rockets for flight

9	Strength
7.5	Speed
8	Agility
5	Intuition
5	Chops
7	Ninjutsu mastery

CHROME DOME

Chrome Dome is an eight-foot-tall (2.4-m-tall) humanoid robot. His android shell resembles samurai armor. Chrome Dome fights with a sword in one hand and a whip in the other. Both weapons glow with plasma energy. He's also equipped with laser-beam eyes. On top of everything else, he can fly using rockets in the soles of his feet.

Who wins? See p. 62!

LEONARDO, RAPHAEL, DONATELLO, MICHELANGELO, SPLINTER, AND APRIL VS. SHREDDER, KARAI, FOOTBOTS, AND KRAANGDROIDS

Master Shredder has one big goal in life: taking revenge on his old rival, Hamato Yoshi. The alien Kraang have a different goal: getting rid of all humans and transforming Earth into a new Kraang homeworld. The Teenage Mutant Ninja Turtles are the one thing standing in the way of both sinister plans. In this matchup, the four Turtles, Splinter, and April O'Neil face off against Shredder and his allies.

SPLINTER, LEONARDO, RAPHAEL, DONATELLO, MICHELANGELO, AND APRIL

The four Ninja Turtle brothers are joined by their sensei-father and April. Because they were all taught by Splinter, the team should work perfectly together. And Master Splinter has even more skills and knowledge. As he once told them, "Everything you know I have taught you, but I have not taught you everything I know."

SPECIES: Turtle-human and human-rat mutants, human
AFFILIATION: Ninja Turtles/Splinter
HOME: Turtles' lair
MAIN WEAPONS: Katana swords, sai, bo staff, nunchuks, tessen fan, and Splinter's staff
SPECIAL SKILLS: Ninjutsu mastery, teamwork, intuition

Strength	7.5
Speed	8
Agility	8.5
Intuition	9
Chops	8.5
Ninjutsu mastery	8.5

THE SHOWDOWN

This is the ultimate matchup, pitting all of the major opponents against each other. The main battle will be between the two masters, Splinter and Shredder. If the Turtles and April can hold Karai at bay long enough to disable the Kraangdroids, the robots' brain-squid operators will flee the scene. But the final outcome is still far from certain.

SPECIES: Human and robot

AFFILIATION: Foot Clan/Shredder and Kraang

HOMES: Shredder's hideout and the TRCI building

MAIN WEAPONS: Tekko-kagi blades, katana sword, circular saw, drill, spiked mace, blasters

SPECIAL SKILLS: Combined mastery of ninjutsu and alien technology

7.5	Strength
7.5	Speed
8	Agility
7	Intuition
6	Chops
7	Ninjutsu mastery

SHREDDER, KARAI, FOOTBOTS, AND KRAANGDROIDS

This team brings Shredder and his Foot Clan together with the mechanical fighters operated by the Kraang. Shredder, Karai, and the FootBots are all experts at ninjutsu. The Kraang in their Kraangbots have a much less refined fighting style: they just fire away with blasters.

Who wins? See p. 62!

THE EXPERTS' PICKS

LEONARDO VS. KARAI
(pp. 8-9)
Winner: **Draw**
Neither ninja gets the upper hand and they reach a standoff at swordpoint. Karai tosses a shuriken at Leo's head. He blocks it, and she escapes.

RAPHAEL VS. DOGPOUND
(pp. 10-11)
Winner: **Raphael**
Dogpound attacks with a barrage of powerful kicks and punches, but Raph's superior speed tires out the mutant dog and decides the fight in the Turtle's favor.

DONATELLO VS. BAXTER STOCKMAN
(pp. 12-13)
Winner: **Donatello**
The battle armor is powerful, but Stockman's reflexes aren't fast enough to keep up with a trained ninja. Donnie slips in to smash the T-Pod, then finishes Stockman off.

MICHELANGELO VS. KRAATHATROGON
(pp. 14-15)
Winner: **Michelangelo**
The Kraathatrogon charges in with gaping jaws. Mikey dodges to the side in the nick of time. He extends his nunchuk chain, hooks the Kraathatrogon, and pulls himself onto its back. He grabs the antennae and rides the worm to a stop.

APRIL O'NEIL VS. FOOT CLAN NINJA
(pp. 16-17)
Winner: **Foot Clan Ninja**
April defends herself well, but the longer reach of the Foot's katana makes it impossible for her to get in an offensive strike with her tessen fan. April retreats.

SPLINTER VS. SHREDDER
(pp. 18-19)
Winner: **Splinter**
Shredder mounts a slashing attack with his tekko-kagi blades. Splinter drops to all fours and darts in to strike the disoriented Shredder from all sides. A final strike drops Shredder.

KIRBY BAT VS. KRAANG
(pp. 20-21)
Winner: **Kirby Bat**
Kirby grabs the squishy brain-squid with his feet, takes off into the air, and lets the Kraang drop. Kirby wins by a fall.

THE NEWTRALIZER VS. TIGER CLAW
(pp. 22-23)
Winner: **The Newtralizer**
Tiger Claw's hot and cold cannons keep the Newtralizer at bay for a time, but the mutant newt soon entangles him with his plasma-rope gun and reels him in like a robot fish.

LEATHERHEAD VS. RAHZAR
(pp. 24-25)
Winner: **Leatherhead**
Rahzar strikes, spins, dodges, and blocks, but his attacks have little effect on the tough-skinned alligator mutant. Leatherhead bides his time until his opponent tires out, then sends the mutant dog off with his tail between his legs.

METALHEAD VS. MOUSERS
(pp. 26-27)
Winner: **MOUSERS**
Metalhead puts up a ferocious fight. MOUSERS go down by the dozen, but their numbers eventually overwhelm the robot ninja.

CASEY JONES VS. KRAANGDROIDS
(pp. 28-29)
Winner: **Casey Jones**
The Kraangdroids stand in a group and fire away with their lasers. Casey dodges and weaves while dropping the robots with a hail of slap shots. He finishes off any Kraangdroids who are still standing with his electric zapper.

APRIL AND DONATELLO VS. FISHFACE
(pp. 30-31)
Winner: **Fishface**
Faced with both an expert ninjutsu attack and snapping, venomous teeth, the teens are forced into a defensive battle and then a retreat.

LEONARDO AND DONATELLO VS. RAPHAEL AND MICHELANGELO
(pp. 32-33)
Winner: **Draw**
Leo beats Michelangelo easily while Raph and Donnie battle it out with sai and bo. But when Leo joins Donnie to help, Michelangelo jumps back into the melee, and the battle rages all over again. Neither team is a clear winner.

APRIL AND CASEY JONES VS. MUTAGEN MAN
(pp. 34-35)
Winners: **April and Casey Jones**
The teenagers split up. Whenever the mutant Timothy goes for one, the other mounts a noisy attack from the rear. Mutagen Man charges back and forth like the ball in a Ping-Pong match until he runs out of mutagen and powers down.

LEONARDO AND RAPHAEL VS. APRIL DERP
(pp. 36-37)
Winner: **April Derp**
Leo and Raph attack with katana swords and sai, but they have a surprisingly difficult time getting past the reach of April Derp's hands, feet, and tentacle-like tongue. In the end, the monster proves too strong, and the Turtles withdraw.

LEONARDO AND DONATELLO VS. RAT KING
(pp. 38-39)
Winner: **Leonardo and Donatello**
Donnie uses his knowledge of rat behavior to distract the rodents with a pile of leftover pizza crusts. Leo takes down the Rat King.

LEONARDO AND MICHELANGELO VS. FOOTBOTS
(pp. 40-41)
Winner: **FootBots**
The Turtles defeat dozens of the robots, but for every FootBot they disable, another takes its place. The Turtles are forced to take off.

RAPHAEL AND DONATELLO VS. FOOT CLAN AND KRAANGDROIDS
(pp. 42-43)
Winner: **Raphael and Donatello**
The Kraangdroids' blasters are of little use in the confusion of Foot Clan and Turtles. Raph and Donnie take out the robots easily, then drive off the Foot Clan.

RAPHAEL AND MICHELANGELO VS. SQUIRRELANOIDS
(pp. 44-45)
Winner: **Raphael and Michelangelo**
The Squirrelanoids go nuts, but Raph fends them off with his sai. Michelangelo extends his nunchuk chain and ties up the rodents.

DONATELLO AND MICHELANGELO VS. SNAKEWEED
(pp. 46-47)
Winner: **Snakeweed**
The Turtles weed-whack Snakeweed, but the mutant plant's tendrils grow back as fast as the ninjas can chop them off, and Donnie and Michelangelo retreat.

RAPHAEL, DONATELLO, AND MICHELANGELO VS. SPIDER BYTEZ AND SPY ROACH
(pp. 48-49)
Winner: **Raphael, Donatello, and Michelangelo**
Raph beats Spider Bytez easily, then helps his brothers exterminate Spy Roach.

LEONARDO, DONATELLO, AND MICHELANGELO VS. RAHZAR AND FISHFACE
(pp. 50-51)
Winner: **Leonardo, Donatello, and Michelangelo**
In the end, the Turtles' three-on-two advantage tips the scales.

LEONARDO, RAPHAEL, AND MICHELANGELO VS. KRAANG BIOTROID
(pp. 52-53)
Winner: **Kraang Biotroid**
The Biotroid whirls like a top, lashing out with fists and saw-tentacles. Leo, Raph, and Michelangelo can't get close enough. When the butt cannons come out, the Turtles beat a hasty retreat.

LEONARDO, RAPHAEL, AND DONATELLO VS. SLASH
(pp. 54-55)
Winner: **Leonardo, Raphael, and Donatello**
Slash takes Donnie and Leo out of the fight. Fueled by anger, Raphael pummels his former pet and turns the match around.

ALL FOUR TURTLES VS. SPLINTER
(pp. 56-57)
Winner: **Splinter**
Leo comes up with a careful plan, sending his brothers and himself in a coordinated attack from four different directions. But Master Splinter seems to be everywhere at once. He blocks every attack. The match ends in the usual way, with Turtles smashing into the walls.

ALL FOUR TURTLES AND APRIL VS. CHROME DOME
(pp. 58-59)
Winner: **Turtles and April**
Chrome Dome gets distracted by his programmed mission to kidnap April. While the robot tries to capture her, the Turtles disable him.

ALL FOUR TURTLES, SPLINTER, AND APRIL VS. SHREDDER, KARAI, FOOTBOTS, AND KRAANGDROIDS
(pp. 60-61)
Winner: **Turtles, Splinter, and April**
The Turtles easily take out the Kraangdroids. With the number of attackers now stacked against them, Shredder and Karai quit the fight.

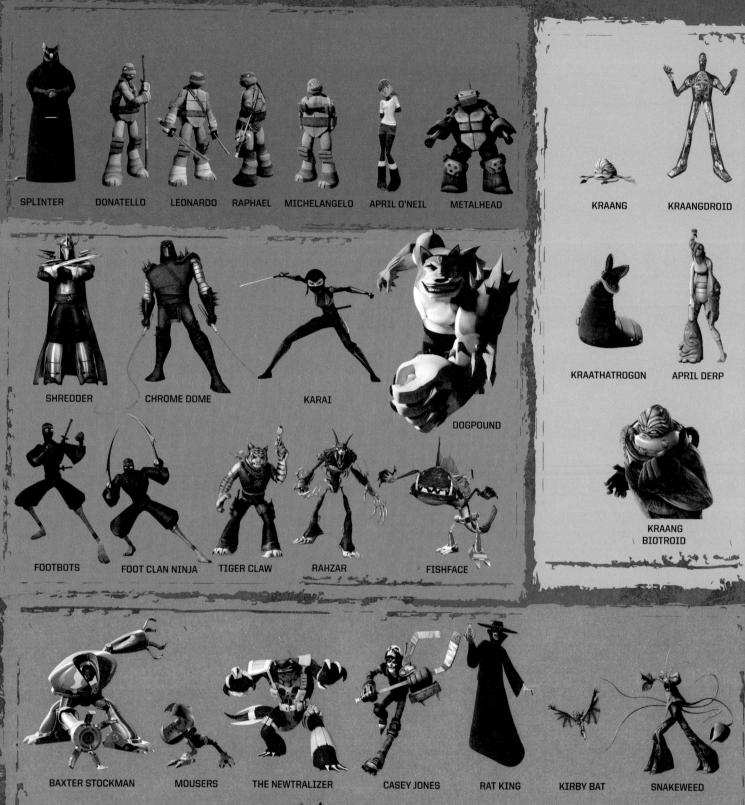

SPLINTER **DONATELLO** **LEONARDO** **RAPHAEL** **MICHELANGELO** **APRIL O'NEIL** **METALHEAD**

KRAANG **KRAANGDROID**

SHREDDER **CHROME DOME** **KARAI**

KRAATHATROGON **APRIL DERP**

DOGPOUND

FOOTBOTS **FOOT CLAN NINJA** **TIGER CLAW** **RAHZAR** **FISHFACE**

KRAANG BIOTROID

BAXTER STOCKMAN **MOUSERS** **THE NEWTRALIZER** **CASEY JONES** **RAT KING** **KIRBY BAT** **SNAKEWEED**

SPY ROACH **SPIDER BYTEZ** **SLASH** **LEATHERHEAD** **SQUIRRELANOID** **MUTAGEN MAN**